SABAH

SABAH

SOUTH CHINA
SEA

SULU SEA

Banggi Is.

KUDAT

Jambongan Is.

Kota Belud

KINABALU PARK
Mt. Kinabalu
4,101 m

Gaya Is.

TURTLE ISLANDS
PARK

Labuk Bay

TUNKU ABDUL
RAHMAN PARK

KOTA KINABALU

Ranau

Sugut River

Labuk River

Sepilok

SANDAKAN

PULAU TIGA
PARK

Kimanis Bay

Tambunan

Mt. Trus Madi

Telupid

Labuan Is.

Beaufort

CROCKER RANGE
NATIONAL PARK

Kinabatangan River

Segama River

Keningau

Weston

LAHAD DATU

Brunei Bay

Tenom

Mt. Rara

Darvel Bay

CELEBES SEA

Mt. Lumaku

Sapulut

TAWAU HILLS
PARK

SEMPORNA

Pensiangan

KALIMANTAN

TAWAU

Sebatik Is.

AMPHIBIANS AND REPTILES
IN SABAH

The Natural History of
AMPHIBIANS AND REPTILES
IN SABAH

Robert F. Inger and Tan Fui Lian

with photographs by
**C.L. Chan, C.M. Clarke, P. Hans Hazebroek,
Gary Heit, W. Hosmer, R.F. Inger,
Wembley Mogindol, Stephen Von Peltz,
W.M. Poon, R.B. Stuebing, Tan Fui Lian,
Tham Nyip Shen and H.K. Voris**

and ink illustrations by
Tan Fui Lian

Natural History Publications (Borneo) Sdn. Bhd.
Kota Kinabalu

1996

Published by

Natural History Publications (Borneo) Sdn. Bhd.,
A913, 9th Floor, Wisma Merdeka,
P.O. Box 13908,
88846 Kota Kinabalu, Sabah, Malaysia.

First published 1996.

The Natural History of Amphibians and Reptiles in Sabah
by Robert F. Inger and Tan Fui Lian

Design and layout by Chua Kok Hian

ISBN 983-812-010-3

Printed and bound in Malaysia
by Print & Co. Sdn. Bhd., Kuala Lumpur.

CONTENTS

Photo: Wembley Mogindol

CHAPTER 1

INTRODUCTION

When people meet us for the first time and learn that we work on amphibians and reptiles, almost always they ask three questions. "Aren't they dangerous? How can you touch those slimy things? Why would anyone be interested in frogs, lizards, and snakes?"

There are poisonous snakes in Sabah, but of the 145 species now known from Borneo only 30 are poisonous and 19 of those live only in the sea. Besides, even those of us who try to find snakes in Bornean forests usually see only one every two days on average. And we are cautious. Lizards will try to bite if you pick them up, but no lizard species in Borneo is poisonous. Some frogs have poison glands in their skins, but cannot squirt it or inject it. Crocodiles are very dangerous, but it takes a determined, knowledgable hunter to find one. The rule is: use common sense. Don't pick up a snake unless you know what species it is. Don't handle lizards carelessly. Don't handle a live frog and then rub your eyes before you wash your hands. And don't play around with crocodiles. The fact is driving a car or smoking are more dangerous to your health than studying amphibians and reptiles. After all, we have been observing and studying these animals for years and are still here to tell the story.

But aren't they slimy? No. Frogs have muscous glands and are usually slightly moist, but not slimy. The glands protect their skin from dessication. Lizards and snakes feel dry. Some lizards have rather hard scales and some, the house geckos, for example, have soft, easily torn skin. A few snakes have rough scales, but most have smooth ones. Where did people get the idea these animals were slimy?

Fig. 1. (Left) Mount Kinabalu. *(Photo: W.M. Poon)*

1

Why would anyone be interested in these animals? There are many reasons. For one thing, their biology is very different from that of birds or mammals, the animals that interest most amateur naturalists, and that difference gives us a perspective on living creatures in general. Some of them are colourful. Some do unexpected things, such as gliding or changing colour. The more we study amphibians and reptiles, the more interesting they seem to us. Like all living things, except ourselves, they exploit their environment efficiently and without damaging it. They have been around for many more millions of years than we have. Maybe they have a few lessons for us.

Those are our reasons. We hope this little book will explain those reasons in more detail and convince its readers that frogs, lizards, and snakes are sometimes beautiful, sometimes surprising, and always worthy of our interest as fellow dwellers on this planet.

Fig. 2. Coastal peat swamp forest. Prime habitat for several species, such as the rough-sided frog *(Rana glandulosa). (Photo: R.F. Inger)*

CHAPTER 2

THE NATURE OF THE BEAST

A mphibians and reptiles, the animals that are the subjects of this book, are two classes of vertebrates, animals with backbones, and in Sabah these animals live in virtually every kind of environment (Figs. 2–9). Amphibia are vertebrates that have managed to evolve into creatures that live on land and breathe air, but that are still tied to water for at least part of their life cycle, like the primitive ancestors of all vertebrates. Reptiles, on the other hand, have lost that dependence on water as an environment by evolving a special membrane around the embryo developing within the egg and by evolving a protective egg shell. In the tropics, these animals occupy a variety of habitats (Figs. 2–9).

Fig. 3. Aerial view of mixed dipterocarp forest in the lowlands. The habitat for most species of amphibians and reptiles in Sabah. *(Photo: C.L. Chan)*

3

Fig. 4. A typical stream in hilly lowland forest: habitat for many species of amphibians and reptiles. *(Photo: R.F. Inger)*

Fig. 5. Rocky stream in the Crocker Range in western Sabah. *(Photo: R.F. Inger)*

Fig. 6. Nipa palm swamp in the estuary of a river along the eastern coast of Sabah: habitat for several species of snakes living in the tidal zone. *(Photo: R.F. Inger)*

Fig. 7. Edge of oak-chestnut lower montane forest. *(Photo: R.F. Inger)*

Fig. 8. Lower Kinabatangan River. Although the habitat has been greatly modified, some species of amphibians and reptiles still manage to exist. *(Photo: R.F. Inger)*

Fig. 9. Completely altered environment near Kota Belud. Only those species adapted to living with man can live in places like this. *(Photo: Tan Fui Lian)*

Fig. 10. *Ichthyophis* species, a caecilian, a limbless amphibian. *(Photo: R.F. Inger)*

Everyone can recognize the commonest form of amphibians, frogs, but in Sabah (and all through Southeast Asia) there is another very obscure type of amphibians, caecilians, and in Europe and North America still a third type, salamanders. Although these three types differ greatly in appearance, they share some fundamental features: As adults they breathe air (like the later evolving vertebrates—reptiles, birds, and mammals). Their eggs have no protective shell (and so are like the eggs of their predecessors, fishes). They have an aquatic larval stage and undergo a metamorphosis or transformation at the end of the larval stage.

In general form, however, these three types of amphibians are radically different. Let's dispose of salamanders first, as they do not occur in Borneo (or its surrounding region) and will not figure further in this book. Salamanders have two pairs of limbs and a tail, like a typical vertebrate. They walk, not leap. Their aquatic larvae look superficially like the adults, except for having external gills, and have diets similar to those of the adults—usually small aquatic insects.

Caecilians (Fig. 10), the second type, at a casual glance look more like earthworms than any kind of vertebrate. They lack limbs and their body is long and worm-like and obviously ringed or segmented like an earthworm. Their eyes are very small and partially hidden under the skin.

Unless one looks very closely, their mouth is not obvious. But they do have a backbone, they do have aquatic larvae that metamorphose into adults, and their eggs lack a protective shell or membrane. One other thing they have—minute scales hidden under the skin—separates them from other living types of amphibians. Caecilians burrow in soil, as adults, or in the sandy beds of small streams, as larvae, so are rarely seen even by herpetologists who spend their time searching through Bornean forests for amphibians and reptiles. Little is known about the details of life of Bornean caecilians, largely because they are so difficult to observe.

No one needs to be told what a frog is. No matter how much the species may differ in size or general shape (Figs. 11–15), we all recognize them as being frogs. But something needs to be said about toads. Strictly speaking, the English word "toad" applies to members of one family of frogs, the family Bufonidae. The anatomical differences between "true" toads and the rest of the frogs are matters mainly of interest to herpetologists. When we use the word "frog" in this book, we include the entire group, even true toads. Frogs feed mainly on insects and other

Fig. 11. *Bufo divergens,* crested toad. *(Photo: R.F. Inger)*

Fig. 12. *Huia cavitympanum,* hole-in-the-head frog. *(Photo: R.F. Inger)*

7

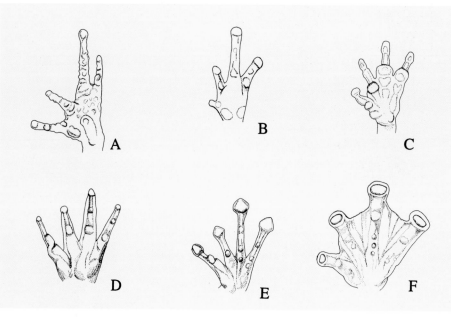

Fig. 13. Underside of hands of frogs. A. *Bufo divergens.* B. *Microhyla borneensis.* C. *Metaphrynella sundana.* D. *Rana ibanorum.* E. *Rana hosii.* F. *Rhacophorus rufipes. (After Inger, 1966)*

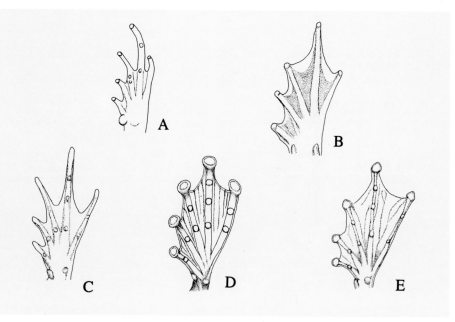

Fig. 14. Underside of feet of frogs. A. *Leptobrachium abbotti.* B. *Bufo divergens.* C. *Rana limnocharis.* D. *Rana hosii.* E. *Rhacophorus rufipes.*

Fig. 15. *Rhacophorus reinwardti,* Reinwardt's flying frog. *(Photo: R.F. Inger)*

Fig. 16. Stages in the
development of a tadpole.

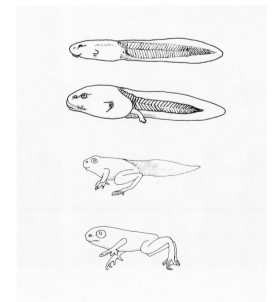

kinds of invertebrates, such as spiders, millipedes, and snails. However, in Sabah a few of the largest species will eat anything they can overpower—other frogs, crabs, small snakes, even small birds. Although most frogs leap, some short-legged (relatively) species in Sabah merely hop or walk and others climb. A few species of tree frogs in Sabah even glide. Altogether, 97 species of frogs have been reported from Sabah and we expect this number to grow.

Most people are also familiar with frog larvae, tadpoles, those odd creatures whose shape, behavior, and life styles are as different as possible from adult frogs. Tadpoles feed on decaying or living vegetation and with that diet comes an extremely long gut—about 10 times the length of the body—which accounts for their fat body. At metamorphosis from tadpole to frog (Figs. 16–17), the gut shortens to about one-fifth its previous length, various other internal organs change, the jaw changes shape, the diet changes to insects, and of course the tail disappears. This metamorphosis is as radical and as significant as that of caterpillar into butterfly.

Four types of reptiles are found in Borneo: crocodiles, turtles, lizards, and snakes. As different as they may appear, they share certain fundamental characters. They all have scales of some form; they all have a three-chambered heart (unlike birds and mammals); they all breathe air throughout their lives; they are all cold-blooded (again unlike birds and mammals); they all have the special egg membrane and shell mentioned above; and unlike amphibians, development does not involve a larval stage.

There are only two species of crocodilians in Borneo, the wide-ranging salt-water crocodile *(Crocodylus porosus)* (Fig. 18), which is certainly capable of eating people, and the false gavial *(Tomistoma schlegelii)*, a smaller, fish-eating, less ferocious member of the group. The false gavial has not been found so far in Sabah. Female crocodilians construct and guard a nest, essentially a pile of vegetation that decays, generating heat and incubating the eggs. The female usually remains near her newly hatched brood until they begin to disperse.

Bornean turtles, though easily recognized by everyone, are a more diverse looking group, with several completely terrestrial species that

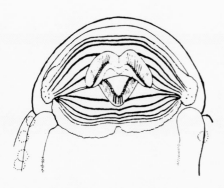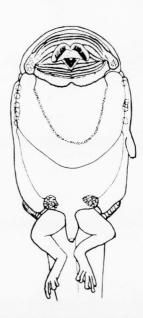

Fig. 17. Tadpole of *Meristogenys orphnocnemis*. Note the sucker on the lower surface (right) that enables this tadpole to cling to rocks in swift water. The beaks (left) are used to scrape algae from rocks.

Fig. 18. *Crocodylus porosus*, the salt-water crocodile. *(Photo: R.B. Stuebing)*

Fig. 19. *Dogania subplana*, the dwarf soft-shelled turtle. *(Photo: R.F. Inger)*

have high-domed shells, a number of semi-aquatic fresh-water species varying in shape (Fig. 19) and four huge sea turtles. Some English books refer to the high-shelled terrestrial turtles as "tortoises" and to certain fresh-water species as "terrapins." We are going to stick to "turtles" for the whole lot. Diets of turtles vary; the terrestrial species and some of the fresh-water and marine species are vegetarians, whereas most of the fresh-water species feed on fishes, crabs, and snails. Female turtles dig nests in sand or soil, cover the nest with the same material after laying their eggs, and then abandon it. The young hatchlings are on their own.

As dissimilar as lizards and snakes appear superficially, certain biologically significant anatomical features of the skull and reproductive structures demonstrate that the two groups share a common ancestor. The superficial differences between lizards and snakes that we all recognize are unreliable in a few cases. We think of lizards as scaly animals (Fig. 21) with two pairs of legs and a tail and as animals that scamper around on the ground (Fig. 20) or sometimes climb up trees (Fig. 22). The trouble with that definition is that it doesn't take into account a few lizards, two of which occur in Sabah, that have gone underground and have lost their legs. Other general differences between lizards and snakes are that lizards can blink their eyes (they have movable eyelids) and they have ear openings on the side of the head (see opening on side of head in Fig. 23). The lizards that have become burrowers have lost the ear opening and the movable eyelids. Despite these exceptions, the general differences hold. Lizards are primarily insectivorous, although the monitor lizards, or "biawak" (Fig. 24), eat larger prey, such as fish, mammals, and birds (including, alas, chickens),

Fig. 20. *Sphenomorphus cyanolaemus,* the blue-sided slender skink. *(Photo: R.F. Inger)*

12

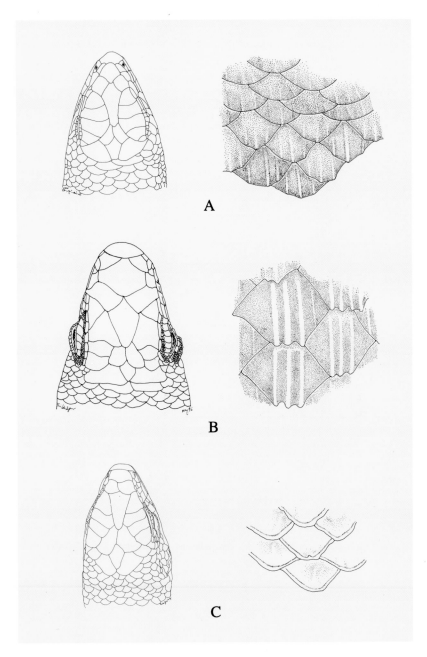

Fig. 21. Scalation of heads (left) and bodies (right) of three species of lizards in the skink family. A. *Apterygodon vittatus.* B. *Mabuya rudis.* C. *Sphenomorphus sabanus.*

Fig. 22. *Gonocephalus doriae*, Doria's anglehead agamid. *(Photo: R.F. Inger)*

Fig. 23. *Mabuya rudis*, the rough-scaled brown skink. *(Photo: R.F. Inger)*

Fig. 24. (Left) *Varanus rudicollis, (Photo: R.F. Inger)*

Fig. 25. (above) *Dendrelaphis caudolineatus,* striped racer. *(Photo: R.F. Inger)*

Fig. 26. (right) *Dendrelaphis caudolineatus* demonstrating the ability of some snakes to climb relatively smooth-barked trees. *(Photo: C.L. Chan)*

and several of the larger geckos will eat small lizards. Female lizards usually lay their eggs in small holes in the ground or under logs of dead leaves on the forest floor, even species that live rather high in trees. Geckos (Figs. 49–50) are the main exceptions, plastering their eggs under bark of a tree trunk, or against the inner wall of a tree hole, or, in the case of house geckos, behind picture frames. The eggs or newly hatched young are not protected. Clutch size varies from two to eight. The 72 species that have been found so far in Sabah range in size from 3.5 cm (without the tail) to more than one metre (the common biawak or monitor lizard).

Despite the fact that snakes are less often seen than lizards, more species of snakes are known from Sabah (119, 15 of them strictly marine) than lizards. A few species live in cultivated fields or around houses; these are the snakes most commonly seen in Sabah. The great majority, however, are confined to Sabah's forests. In size these species vary from the tiny blind snakes scarcely 30 cm long to the giant reticulated python, which certainly reaches more than 6 metres; most are in the 0.5–1.5 metre range. Many of Sabah's snakes live underground or under rocks or decaying logs, such as the small reed snakes (Fig. 27), others live at the surface level (Figs. 25–26), and still others spend their time in shrubs and trees (Fig. 28). All Bornean snakes feed on living prey, which vary in size from earthworms, spiders, and snails to frogs, lizards, small mammals, and birds. As one might expect, only the smallest species feed on spiders and earthworms, while the large species feed on mammals. With few exceptions, Bornean snakes are egg-layers with clutch sizes varying from three to twelve. We assume that most of them lay their eggs on the ground under dead leaves or in crevices, but very little is known about the details of their breeding habits. The exceptions, live-bearing snakes, are mainly the marine sea-snakes.

One of the first questions most people ask about a snake is: "Is it poisonous?" Of the 104 species of Bornean snakes that live on land or in fresh water, only 11 are seriously dangerous to human beings. Some people think that poisonous snakes can be recognized by the shape of their head, that poisonous snakes have triangular heads and non-venomous ones do not. That is only partially correct. In the drawings of Figs. 31 and 32, we show the shape and scalation of the heads of a typical non-poisonous snake (a rat snake, *Elaphe)*, a poisonous pit-viper

Fig. 27. *Calamaria lumbricoidea,* a reed snake. *(Photo: R.F. Inger)*

Fig. 28. *Boiga jaspidea,* mottled cat snake. *(Photo: R.F. Inger)*

Fig. 29. *Tropidolaemus wagleri,* keeled Malaysian pit-viper. *(Photo: Hans Hazebroek)*

(Tropidolaemus wagleri) and perhaps the most dangerous one of all, a king cobra *(Ophiophagus hannah)*. Pit-vipers (Fig. 29) do have a triangular head quite different from the rat snake, but the king cobra (Fig. 30) does not. The king cobra does have a pair of unique, enlarged scales at the rear of the head (Fig. 32) that distinguish it from the rat snake, but few of us would want to get close enough to the cobra to examine its head scales. Since the chance of encountering any snake is rather small, the chance of seeing a poisonous snake is extremely low. Nevertheless, should you see a snake, do not pick it up unless you are absolutely certain of its identity. Should you by accident be bitten by a snake, get to the emergency room of the nearest hospital. But do not exaggerate the danger from snakes—the car you drive is far more dangerous.

Fig. 30. *Ophiophagus hannah,* king cobra. *(Photo: S. Von Peltz)*

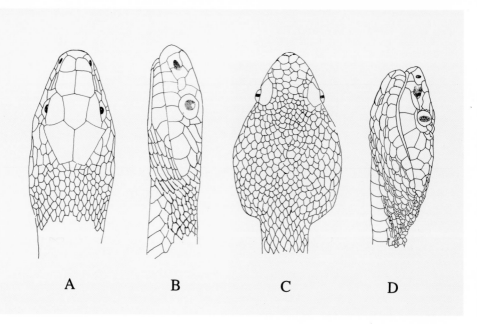

Fig. 31. Head scalation of a rat snake *(Elaphe)* (A & B) and a pit-viper *(Trimeresurus sumatranus)*. (C & D). (Rat snake reprinted from M.W.F. Tweedie, *The Snakes of Malaya*; drawings of pit-viper by Tan Fui Lian)

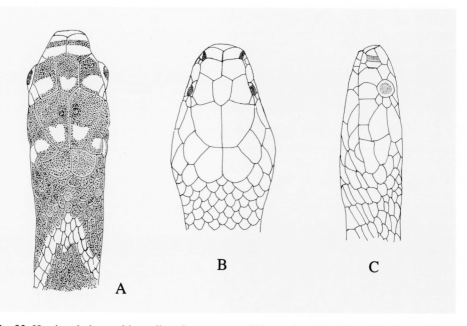

Fig. 32. Head scalation and juvenile colour pattern of king cobra (A). The conspicuous yellow rings of the juvenile fade and the snake becomes completely dark as it matures. (Reprinted from M.W.F. Tweedie, *The Snakes of Malaya*)

CHAPTER 3

AMPHIBIANS AND REPTILES OF THE COASTAL ZONE

T he coast of Sabah is fringed with small rocky islands, rich coral reefs, rocky or muddy shallows, sandy beaches in some places and mangrove marshes in others. Each of these distinctive environments is home to particular kinds of reptiles. In terms of species, sea snakes are the dominant reptiles around rocky islands and coral reefs where they find their fish prey. Only one group of sea snakes, the sea kraits, genus *Laticauda,* crawls out on land. One of these species, the yellow-lipped sea krait *Laticauda colubrina* (Fig. 33) can be seen in large numbers on a tiny rocky island, Pulau Kampunian Damit; the Snake Island, as it is often called, is part of Pulau Tiga Park. It is not

Fig. 33. *Laticauda,* sea krait. *(Photo: H.K. Voris)*

Fig. 34. (right) *Enhydrina,* beaked sea snake. *(Photo: H.K. Voris)*

Fig. 35. *Chelonia mydas,* green sea turtle. *(Photo: C.L. Chan)*

unusual to see 150 of these black-banded snakes in a single day, curled up in rocky crevices. It feeds exclusively on eels which they hunt in the coral reefs surrounding Pulau Tiga.

The diets of the rest of the sea snakes consist of a variety of marine life. Several species prey only on eels, which they locate by probing burrows and coral crevices with their very slender heads and necks. There are other odd dietary specialists among these snakes. The beaked sea snake *Enhydrina schistosa* (Fig. 34), for example, eats spiny sea catfishes almost exclusively. But the oddest diet, considering that all sea snakes have fangs with which to inject poison and immobilise prey, is that of the olive sea snake *Aipysurus eydouxi* (Fig. 36); it eats nothing but fish eggs.

Small islands with sandy beaches invite a very different kind of reptile, sea turtles. These giants among living turtles—shell length over 1.5 metres—crawl out of the sea to excavate their nests and lay their eggs, then crawl laboriously back into the sea. One of the most amazing natural history sights in Sabah is to watch the parade of nesting green sea turtles, *Chelonia mydas* (Fig. 35), at night on the Turtle Islands, another of Sabah's parks. The female digs the nest using her hind flippers, lays

Fig. 36. *Aipysurus eydouxi,* olive sea snake. *(Photo: H.K. Voris)*

her eggs, and covers the nest by throwing sand over the site with her large front flippers. When she returns to the sea, the turtle is met by smaller males eager to mate. After mating, the female may return to the beach in a week or so to lay another clutch of eggs. Or she may swim off and not return to nest until two or three years later. A somewhat smaller species, the hawksbill sea turtle, *Eretmochelys imbricata* (Fig. 37) also nests on the Turtle Islands. There are three other species of sea turtles in Sabah waters—the olive Ridley sea turtle *(Lepidochelys olivaceus)*, which is much smaller than the green sea turtle, the large (up to 2 m) loggerhead *(Caretta caretta)*, and the really gigantic leatherback sea turtle, *Dermochelys coriacea,* topping 2.5 m and 700 kilos. Not much is known about the nesting of the last three in Sabah. The green sea turtle feeds mainly on algae and the leatherback mainly on jellyfish. The other three eat some algae but subsist largely on invertebrates—molluscs, jellyfish, sea cucumbers, etc. They all seem unaffected by the stinging cells of jellyfish.

Sea turtles have always had economic value in Sabah and other parts of their distributions. In the past, they were killed in large numbers for their meat. Their principal monetary value now comes from their pingpong-ball-sized eggs, which are an important item of commerce all through Southeast Asia. Entire small communities in Sabah are supported by harvesting the eggs; a single nest can contain 50–150 eggs. This harvest is now very tightly regulated by Sabah Parks to ensure the long-term survival of the species and the crop of eggs. The shell of the hawksbill is the source of tortoise shell combs and other fineries. The trade in this material became so important that the hawksbill was on the verge of extinction.

In tidal estuaries, where large, muddy rivers meet the sea, mangrove swamps and broad, muddy tidal flats form another important environment for a variety of animals including snakes and turtles. The file snake, *Acrochordus granulosus,* an ugly brown or dark gray snake with very rough scales, is very abundant in these shallow waters where is feeds mainly on fishes that occupy burrows. Occasionally, the file snake is found 1–2 km off the coast in relatively shallow waters, but a species of a different group, the dog-faced snake *Cerberus rhynchops,* which is also very common on the mudflats and adjoining mangrove swamps, is strictly limited to inshore environments. When the tide is out

Fig. 37. *Eretmochelys imbricata.* hawksbill turtle, source of tortoise shell of commerce. *(Photo: Gary Heit)*

exposing mudflats the dog-faced snake is busy chasing its prey, mainly mudskippers, those odd fishes that scoot around over mudflats looking for small crabs. Both the file snake and the dog-faced snake are live bearing, with brood size of about 5 in the former and 10–27 in the latter. A relative of the dog-faced snake, the crab-eating snake, *Fordonia leucobalia*, also lives in mangrove swamps makes its living eating crabs. Several snakes that are common in lowland forests (see next chapter) also live in mangrove swamps. In fact, one, *Boiga dendrophila*, gets its common name, the mangrove snake, from its occurrence in this environment.

Large muddy estuaries provide a haven for three large non-marine species of turtles. The largest, the Asian giant soft-shelled turtle, *Pelochelys bibroni*, grows to about one metre and feeds on fish, shrimp, crabs, and molluscs. The other two estuarine turtles, the painted terrapin, *Callagur borneoensis*, and the river terrapin, *Batagur baska*, are almost purely vegetarian although the river terrapin also eats snails. Both of the terrapins grow to a shell length between 50 and 70 cm, and males of both have unusual colouration during the breeding season. Most of the year the river terrapin is olive gray, but when breeding the head, neck, and legs turn black and the iris of the eye changes from yellowish to white. The head in breeding males of the painted terrapin becomes white with a red stripe between the eyes.

In peninsular Malaysia collection of the eggs of both terrapins was once very important. But the populations have declined dramatically, perhaps to only one-tenth of their pre-World War II sizes. Probably both over-collecting of eggs and flooding of nesting sites by damming of rivers have contributed to the declines.

Man is not the only predator of these large turtles. Large estuaries are also the main hunting and breeding grounds of the salt-water crocodile, *Crocodylus porosus,* which includes turtles in its broad diet. Attempts to study the numbers and behavior of adult crocodiles in Sabah's rivers have had limited success. Hatchlings and young crocs can be caught and marked with tags from boats at night, using a bright light to shine at the crocs' eyes. But it seems that by the time one of these crocs reaches 2 m, it becomes smart enough to dive or otherwise escape detection. The discovery of nests, masses of decaying vegetation, is proof of a continuing population. The crocs are not limited to the coastal zone, but also move up the largest muddy rivers well above the tidal zone and form one of the minor but real hazards of life for villagers on these rivers.

Amphibians haven't been mentioned in this chapter to this point and for a good reason. Brackish water is deadly for the frogs of Southeast Asia except for one species, the crab-eating frog, *Rana cancrivora.* Adults of this species have been shown to tolerate water that is 80% the salinity of pure sea water. Their tadpoles have even greater tolerance—up to 120% salinity of sea water. Apparently, these frogs do not swallow water when they are in brackish water.

The coastal zone is clearly a place for narrowly specialized species of reptiles. Although none of them is limited in its distribution to Sabah, they do form a remarkable assemblage that merits conservation at least because of their economic value but also because they represent some ancient evolutionary lineages.

CHAPTER 4

AMPHIBIANS AND REPTILES
IN LOWLAND FORESTS

The lowland forests of Sabah, that is, the forests that lie between the tidal zone (say, about 5 m above sea level) and the lower montane zone (say, to about 800 m above sea level) provide the living space for most of the species of amphibians and reptiles. Here, where plant life is richest, the fauna also reaches its greatest diversity. There is even diversity from place to place, for this largest part of Sabah includes environments of different types.

Basically, the major kinds of habitats in this lowland zone depend on the terrain. Flat areas, such as those along the Kinabatangan River, have deep soil, turbid streams with muddy bottoms, and numerous small, rain-filled depressions. On the other hand, the steep slopes of the Crocker Range running parallel to the West Coast have forests with rather shallow soil, clear rocky streams with strong current, and very few small ponds.

Peat swamp fauna

One flat corner of Sabah, the southern part of the West Coast near Weston, has a very special environment, a peat swamp forest. It is as different from the well-drained forest of the Crocker Range as can be imagined. The amphibians and reptiles of Bornean peat swamps (Fig. 38) have not been studied as much as the fauna of other lowland forests, probably because it is not a very inviting place to live in. Still it has its own special interests. Because the swamp is so close to sea level, water moves through it slowly. All the streams are sluggish and have muddy bottoms. There are many small ponds. But what really sets the aquatic habitats of the peat swamp apart is the high acidity of the water. One of

Fig. 38. (Above) Bornean peat swamp forest. *(Photo: Hans Hazebroek)*

Fig. 39. (Above) *Bufo quadriporcatus*, swamp toad. *(Photo: R.F. Inger)*

Fig. 40. (Right) *Rana glandulosa*, rough-sided frog. *(Photo: R.F. Inger)*

28

our colleagues remarked after testing the water, "Battery acid!" How this character of the water affects survival of tadpoles is not known with certainty, but it must have some effect for the frog fauna of these peat swamps is somewhat different from that of the better drained forests. In other parts of the world, the eggs of some species of frogs are killed when placed in water with a low pH, which indicates rather acidic conditions.

Most of the species we might call peat swamp specialists are frogs. That is not surprising considering that, of the animals this book deals with, only frogs have a necessary aquatic stage and a skin that is permeable and cannot protect them from the direct effects of the acidic water. The frogs that do well in this environment include a wide range of behavioral types. The swamp toad, *Bufo quadriporcatus* (Fig. 39), lives on the forest floor like every good toad should and deposits its eggs in small ponds. Other ground frogs in these swamps include the rough-sided frog, *Rana glandulosa* (Fig. 40), which croaks from tangles of roots and dead leaves around the bases of trees, and the yellow-bellied mud frog, *Occidozyga laevis*. The masked frog *Rana paramacrodon,* another ground dwelling frog, is mainly confined to the banks of sluggish swamp streams. A smaller version of the rough-sided frog, the swamp frog (*Rana baramica* Fig. 41) calls mainly from stumps and small trees and vines, about 1–2 m above ground. These swamps are also prime habitat for several tree frogs—the frilled tree frog, *Rhacophorus appendiculatus* (Fig. 42), and Collett's tree frog, *Polypedates colletti* (Fig. 43). Females

Fig. 41. *Rana baramica,* swamp frog. *(Photo: R.F. Inger)*

Fig. 42. *Rhacophorus appendiculatus,* frilled tree frog. *(Photo: C.L. Chan)*

Fig. 43. (Left) *Polypedates colletti,* Collett's tree frog. *(Photo: R.F. Inger)*

of both of these species form sticky foam nests as the eggs are extruded and these nests are attached to vegetation overhanging water. The frilled tree frog suspends its foam nests over very shallow water; when the tadpoles hatch, they drop into the 2 to 5 cm of water where they complete their development. Collett's tree frog, on the other hand, hangs its foam nests over deeper pools, usually at least 20 cm deep. Its tadpoles are much larger than those of the frilled tree frog and apparently need greater volumes of water for proper development.

Relatively little is known about the lizards and snakes of the peat swamps, but the information available suggests that as a group they are not much different from the array of species one might find in other lowland forests. Certainly the black and yellow mangrove snake, *Boiga dendrophila* (Fig. 44), is at home here. Water snakes of several types, including the dog-faced snake (*Cerberus rhynchops*), the white-fronted water snake, *Amphiesma flavifrons* (Fig. 45), and the red-sided water snake

Fig. 44. *Boiga dendrophila,* mangrove snake. *(Photo: W. Hosmer)*

30

Fig. 45. *Amphiesma flavifrons,* white-fronted water snake. *(Photo: R.F. Inger)*

(*Xenochrophis trianguligera,* Fig. 46), are relatively common and secretive reed snakes of the genera *Calamaria* (Fig. 27) and *Pseudorabdion* find their earthworm prey under debris on dry portions of the swamp forest floor.

Of the lizards that are active by day, the skinks living at ground level are the most conspicuous. The rough-scaled brown skink, *Mabuya rudis,* and one of the fine-scaled slender skinks, *Sphenomorphus multisquamatus* (Fig. 47), have been seen in Sabah's peat swamps, but they are widely distributed in Sabah's forests. The banded flying lizard,

Draco quinquefasciatus and others of this group have no trouble finding suitable living space on the trunks of the larger trees in these swamps. The comb-crested agamid, *Gonocephalus liogaster* (Fig. 48), is also at home up in the trees, though it is not as restricted to large tree trunks as the flying lizards. As all of these lizards lay their eggs on the ground under dead leaves or

Fig. 46. *Xenochrophis trianguligera,* red-sided water snake. *(Photo: W. Hosmer)*

31

Fig. 47. (Right) *Sphenomorphus multisquamatus,* fine-scaled slender skink. *(Photo: R.F. Inger)*

Fig. 48A. (Above) *Gonocephalus liogaster* (juvenile). *(Photo: Tham Nyip Shen)*

Fig. 48B. (Right) *Gonocephalus liogaster,* comb-crested agamid (adult). *(Photo: R.B. Stuebing)*

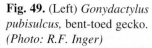

Fig. 49. (Left) *Gonydactylus pubisulcus,* bent-toed gecko. *(Photo: R.F. Inger)*

Fig. 50. (Right) *Gonydactylus consobrinus,* giant bent-toed gecko. *(Photo: R.B. Stuebing)*

in small, shallow holes, the normally saturated soil of the swamp may limit opportunities for breeding. The nocturnal geckos have no trouble of that sort as they often stick their eggs (always laid in pairs) under bark above ground or in dry tree holes. One of the common geckos of these swamps is a small bent-toed gecko, *Gonydactylus pubisulcus* (Fig. 49), which prefers to clamber about on leaves and stems of shrubs and small trees, those usually less than 20 cm in diameter. This preference may be a means of avoiding its much larger relative *Gonydactylus consobrinus* (Fig. 50), which lives on very large tree trunks and preys upon small lizards as well as large insects.

One of the interesting questions about the fauna of the peat swamp in Sabah concerns species that have **not** been found there. In the peat swamps of Sarawak to the south, we have found several species of frogs that are known elsewhere only from peninsular Malaysia—the Malaysian greater swamp frog, *Rana malesiana,* and the black-eyed litter frog, *Leptobrachium nigrops.* There is no reason why these frogs should not also occur in peat swamp in Sabah. But do they? Certain species of turtles, such as the Malayan box turtle *Cuora amboinensis* (Fig. 51) and the Asian leaf turtle *Cyclemys dentata* (Fig. 52), which are widespread in flat areas, have not yet been recorded from peat swamp forest, though they must be there. Clearly, much remains to be learned about the animals in the peat swamp forests.

Fig. 51. (Left) *Cuora amboinensis,* Malayan box turtle. *(Photo: W.M. Poon)*

Fig. 52. (Below) *Cyclemys dentata,* Asian leaf turtle. *(Photo: W.M. Poon)*

Flat lowland forest

Areas of flat forest (Fig. 53) at slightly higher elevations than the peat swamp have a much richer and a better known fauna. As is true in any Bornean forest, there is a daily pace to life that applies to the amphibians and reptiles as much as to, say, birds. Shortly after dawn, even before the ground mist (Fig. 54) rises, the slender skinks of the genus *Sphenomorphus* (Fig. 55) become active. They move away from the base of tree buttresses, where so many kinds of skinks seem to retreat at night, and begin to forage for insects over the dead leaves and logs that litter the forest floor. They seem to do best when their body temperatures can be maintained at about 25°–27°C (77°–80°F), and so do well before the sun gets very high in the sky. Remember that reptiles are cold-blooded which means they get their body heat from the environment. To avoid over-heating a slender skink has to avoid the sun.

Fig. 53. Interior of flat lowland rain forest. *(Photo: Hans Hazebroek)*

Fig. 54. (Left) Morning mist in lowland rain forest. *(Photo: R.F. Inger)*

Fig. 55. (Below) *Sphenomorphus sabanus*, Sabah slender skink. *(Photo: R.F. Inger)*

Fig. 56. (Left) *Mabuya rudis*, rough-scaled brown skink. *(Photo: C.L. Chan)*

After the mist is cleared by the sun, about 8.30–9.00 a.m. in the forests along the east coast, the larger rough-scaled brown skinks, *Mabuya rudis,* (Fig. 56) move out of their night resting places under logs or at the bases of trees into sun spots on the forest floor in order to bask and soak up the warmth of the sun. Only when they have raised their body temperatures to about 32°–36°C (90°–96°F), their best operating level, do they begin to forage for food, threaten other rough skinks that may be in the wrong home territory, or court females. At about the same time, up in the crowns of trees, the flying lizards (genus *Draco*) respond to the rising temperatures and start their hunt for ants and termites moving up the trunks of large trees. Some snakes are also active in the morning, but these are mainly secretive species, such as the red-necked reed snake *Pseudorabdion collaris* (Fig. 57) crawling under logs or under forest floor litter where there is little difference between night and day.

Fig. 57. *Pseudorabdion collaris,* red-necked reed snake. *(Photo: R.F. Inger)*

At mid-day if one walks along a forest trail, past a sun fleck, one may hear a rustling of dead leaves as a brown skink is frightened and scuttles off. Or, by looking carefully at tree trunks about 8–12 m above the ground, one may spot a flying lizard flashing its conspicuously coloured throat dewlap warning other males that it is defending its territory. Snakes are almost never seen at this time of day. Occasionally, a green vine snake may be seen in low vegetation as it hunts for lizards.

As the sun sets, the skinks retreat into their resting places and flying lizards move to the tips of slender twigs or hanging vines for the night. When darkness falls, about 6.30–7.00 p.m., life begins for most of Sabah's frogs, snakes, and one group of lizards, the geckos. Far in the forest, away from any stream, frogs begin to call around pools or seepage

Fig. 58. (Left) Rhino wallow in lowland rain forest, important breeding site for several species of frogs. *(Photo: R.F. Inger)*

Fig. 59. (Right) *Rhacophorus dulitensis,* jade tree frog. *(Photo: R.F. Inger)*

areas. Rain-filled wild boar or rhino wallows (Fig. 58), usually 2–4 m across, provide ideal breeding places for many species of tree frogs, including the jade frog (*Rhacophorus dulitensis,* Fig. 59), Wallace's flying frog (*Rhacophorus nigropalmatus,* Fig. 60), the masked tree frog (*Polypedates macrotis,* Fig. 62), and the file-eared frog (*Polypedates otilophus,* Fig. 61). But terrestrial frogs, such as the squat brown bullfrog *Kaloula baleata* (Fig. 63), and the yellow-bellied mud frog (*Occidozyga laevis*) also use these wallows. At night one can

Fig. 60. *Rhacophorus nigropalmatus,* Wallace's flying frog. *(Photo: R.F. Inger)*

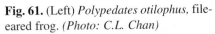

Fig. 61. (Left) *Polypedates otilophus*, file-eared frog. *(Photo: C.L. Chan)*

Fig. 62. (Right) *Polypedates macrotis*, masked tree frog. *(Photo: R.F. Inger)*

Fig. 63. (Below) *Kaloula baleata*, brown bullfrog. *(Photo: R.F. Inger)*

Fig. 64. *Chaperina fusca,* saffron-bellied frog. *(Photo: R.B. Stuebing)*

see the larger tadpoles of the tree frogs come to the surface of the turbid water to gulp air and dive back into the murky water. This is also the kind of micro-habitat where one is likely to see the red-sided water snake (*Xenochrophis trianguligera* Fig. 46), which feeds almost exclusively on frogs; very young *Xenochrophis* prey on tadpoles.

At very small pools, those about 25–30 cm across, so filled with decaying vegetation that the water smells putrid, the tiny saffron-bellied frog *Chaperina fusca* (Fig. 64) gathers; its low buzz sounds almost insect-like. Tadpoles of *Chaperina* are very small, at most 1 cm long, and hang in mid-water filtering water through their gill baskets and subsisting quite well on the minute fungi and bacteria they trap in this manner. It is astonishing how many *Chaperina* tadpoles can live in one of these small pools.

Most species of snakes hunt for food at night. The best way to see snakes, or other creatures for that matter, in these flat forests is to take a night-time stroll along a trail. The commonest snakes on the forest floor are two small (never more than 40 cm) species, the slug-eater *Pareas*

Fig. 65. *Pareas laevis,* slug-eating snake. *(Photo: R.F. Inger)*

41

Fig. 68. (Right) *Aplopeltura boa*, feeding on snail. *(Photo: C.L. Chan)*

Fig. 66. (Left) *Lycodon subcinctus,* banded wolf snake. *(Photo: C.L. Chan)*

Fig. 67. (Below) *Aeluroscalabotes felinus,* cat gecko. *(Photo: R.F. Inger)*

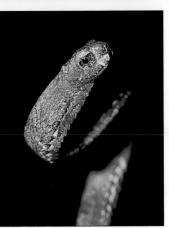

laevis (Fig. 65) and the banded wolf snake, *Lycodon subcinctus* (Fig. 66). In low shrubs, the snail-eating snake *Aplopeltura boa* (Figs. 68–69) stretches out to bridge the space from branch to branch as it searches for it prey. This is also the best way to see nocturnal lizards, such as the cat gecko *Aeluroscalabotes felinus* (Fig. 67), usually on dead logs or in shrubs; one of the bent-toed geckos, *Gonydactylus* (Fig. 71), usually on

Fig. 69. (Left) *Aplopeltura boa,* snail-eating snake. *(Photo: R.F. Inger)*

43

Fig. 70. (Above) *Phoxophrys nigrilabris,* bush agamid. *(Photo: R.F. Inger)*

Fig. 71. (Above) *Gonydactylus ingeri,* Sabah bent-toed gecko. *(Photo: C.L. Chan)*

Fig. 72. (Right) *Ptychozoon kuhli,* Kuhl's gliding gecko. *(Photo: R.F. Inger)*

Fig. 73. (Left) *Metaphrynella sundana,* Bornean tree-hole frog. *(Photo: R.B. Stuebing)*

medium-sized trees; and occasionally a gliding gecko, *Ptychozoon kuhli* (Fig. 72). Night is also the best time to find the small bush agamid, *Phoxophrys nigrilabris* (Fig. 70), as it sleeps on the tips of branches.

Mixed among the insect sounds are the piping notes of the Bornean tree-hole frog *Metaphrynella sundana* (Fig. 73). Males of this small (2 cm) frog sit in water-containing holes of small trees (less than 20 cm in diameter); it is possible to hear the call of this species from the same tree hole night after night. Apparently, the rule is: if you find a good tree hole, stick with it.

Fig. 74. (Above) *Rhacophorus kajau,* charming leaf frog. *(Photo: R.F. Inger)*

45

Shallow marshes are common in these flat lowlands and are the kind of habitat favored by the Malayan box turtle *Cuora amboinensis.* This completely herbivorous species is the only turtle in Sabah that has a light stripe on each side of the top of the head, making it easy to identify. It gets its common name from its ability to close the shell opening with its hinged lower shell.

Fig. 75. *Rana ingeri,* greater swamp frog. *(Photo: R.F. Inger)*

These marshes are also home to large populations of frogs and tadpoles. The most conspicuous, because of their calls, are tree frogs, such as the frilled tree frog and the tiny charming tree frog *Rhacophorus kajau* (Fig. 74). The tadpoles of these tree frogs seem to be confined to water not much over 2 cm deep. A number of other frogs are attracted to these shallow swampy areas for breeding sites, for example, the yellow-bellied mud frog *Occidozyga laevis* and the harlequin tree frog (*Rhacophorus pardalis* Fig. 76). But at least one species, the greater swamp frog *Rana ingeri* (Fig. 75), is there to prey on crabs and other frogs. Where there are frogs, there are certain to be snakes that prey on them. One of the commonest in these situations is the small (less than one metre long)

46

mock viper *Psammodynastes pulverulentus* (Fig. 77), which has not the slightest hesitancy to bite anyone who tries to grab it; fortunately it is not poisonous, though its long sharp teeth deliver a painful puncture wound. The red-sided water snake, which we have already mentioned, is also common in these marshy areas.

Fig. 76. *Rhacophorus pardalis,* harlequin tree frog. *(Photo: R.B. Stuebing)*

Small streams, which in these flat areas often have steep mud

Fig. 77. *Psammodynastes pulverulentus,* mock viper. *(Photo: C.L. Chan)*

47

Fig. 78. *Rana signata,* spotted stream frog. *(Photo: R.F. Inger)*

Fig. 79. *Rana blythi,* Blyth's frog. *(Photo: R.F. Inger)*

Fig. 80. (Right) *Rana chalconota,* white-lipped frog. *(Photo: R.F. Inger)*

Fig. 81. (Below) Stream in hilly lowland rain forest. More species of frogs breed along such streams than at any other type of habitat in Borneo. *(Photo: R.F. Inger)*

banks, are sometimes noisy places at night. The frogs that contribute the most to the chorus along these streams are the spotted stream frog *Rana signata* (Fig. 78), calling its multi-note harsh chirp usually from below a projecting tree root, and the white-lipped frog *Rana chalconota* (Fig. 80) emitting its staccato clicking notes from low shrubs lining the bank. Also living along these muddy banks are much larger frogs that do not call, Blyth's frog *Rana blythi* (Fig. 79). Sometimes reaching a body length of 17–20 cm, Blyth's frog is a formidable predator on frogs, large invertebrates, such as large millipeds and crabs, and even small snakes.

Fig. 82. Rocky stream in foothills of mountains, another important breeding site for frogs. *(Photo: Hans Hazebroek)*

Hilly rain forest fauna

Where the landscape becomes hilly with gentle or steep slopes is the forest that houses the greatest diversity of amphibians and reptiles. Basically, that diversity depends on the variety of microhabitats available. There are streams of all types, from trickles to major rivers, from sandy-bottom creeks (Fig. 81) to rushing, tumbling, rocky creeks (Fig. 82). Seepages of water emerge at the base of some hills. Where the slope is gentle, there are scattered, small rain-filled ponds. Vertical layers of habitats are conspicuous. There are tall trees bearing epiphytes, shrubs, low herbs and seedlings, and at the ground level a layer of dead leaves with scattered decaying logs. The huge trees with large buttresses (Fig. 83) provide special niches that collect dead leaves. Each of these layers has its own small "microclimate." The amounts of light and breeze increase, of course, from the

Fig. 83. (Left) Tree buttresses in lowland rain forest. Many lizards and small snakes take shelter in such places. *(Photo: R.F. Inger)*

Fig. 84. (Above) *Apterygodon vittatus,* striped tree skink. *(Photo: R.B. Stuebing)*

ground to the tree crowns. Temperature follows the same rule, being generally cooler and varying less near the ground than higher in the trees.

The variety of microhabitats gives an opportunity for animals to specialize and in effect divide the resources of the environment. For example, among the diurnal lizards, the flying lizards (genus *Draco*) occupy the trunks of the largest trees, the larger angleheads (genus *Gonocephalus*) live mainly on small trees, and the much smaller purple-mouthed bush agamid (*Phoxophrys nigrilabris,* Fig. 70) lives in shrubs. At night, geckos also split this way: the giant bent-toed gecko (*Gonydactylus consobrinus,* Fig. 50) lives on the trunks of the largest trees and the smaller species of the genus on small trees. There is a comparable division of the forest on the basis of position in the vertical column, with the rough-scaled brown skink *(Mabuya rudis)* and slender skinks *(Sphenomorphus)* living on the ground, the striped tree skink (*Apterygodon vittatus,* Fig. 84) from ground level to tree crowns, and green tree skink *(Dasia olivacea)* only in the tree crowns. Sticking to

Fig. 85. (Above) *Gonocephalus doriae,* Doria's anglehead agamid. *(Photo: R.F. Inger)*

Fig. 86. (Above) *Gonocephalus grandis,* creek anglehead agamid. *(Photo: C.L. Chan)*

Fig. 87. (Right) *Gonocephalus grandis. (Photo: R.F. Inger)*

Fig. 88. *Rhabdophis chrysarga,* speckled-bellied keelback. *(Photo: R.F. Inger)*

lizards, there are even differences between species in sleeping places. At night, the Doria's anglehead agamid (*Gonocephalus doriae,* Fig. 85) sleeps pressed against the base of small trees, but the creek anglehead agamid (*G. grandis,* Figs. 86–87) sleeps clinging to the tips of slender twigs overhanging water into which it will dive if danger threatens.

Snakes divide the forest in similar ways. The reed snakes (*Calamaria* and *Pseudorabdion*) burrowing into soil crevices or under rotting leaves and logs, the smooth snakes (*Liopeltis*), speckled-bellied keelback (*Rhabdophis chrysarga,* Fig. 88), and the coral snakes (*Maticora,* Fig.

Fig. 89. (Right) *Trimeresurus puniceus,* leaf-nosed pit-viper. *(Photo: R.F. Inger)*

Fig. 90. (Below) *Ahaetulla prasina,* green vine snake. *(Photo: C.L. Chan)*

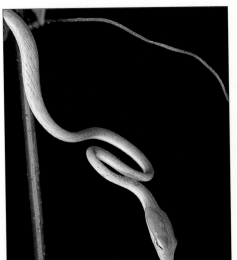

Fig. 91. (Above) *Maticora bivirgata,* striped Oriental coral snake. *(Photo: R.F. Inger)*

Fig. 92. *Gonyophis margaritatus*, rainbow tree snake. *(Photo: R.F. Inger)*

Fig. 93. *Zaocys fuscus*, brown rat snake. *(Photo: R.B. Steubing)*

91) on the forest floor; the green vine snake (*Ahaetulla prasina*, Fig. 90) and the leaf-nosed pit-viper (*Trimeresurus puniceus*, Fig. 89) in shrubs and low trees; and the rainbow tree snake (*Gonyophis margaritatus*, Fig. 92) up in the larger trees. A few species, such as the reticulated python (Fig. 96) and the very large (often more than 2.5 m) brown rat snake (*Zaocys fuscus*, Fig. 93) commonly move from ground level to tree

Fig. 94. (Above left) *Boiga cynodon,* dog-toothed cat snake. *(Photo: C.L. Chan)*

Fig. 95. (Above right) *Python curtus,* blood python. *(Photo: S. Von Peltz)*

Fig. 96. (Right) *Python reticulatus,* reticulated python. *(Photo: S. Von Peltz)*

crown and from forest to river bank. The blood python, *Python curtus* (Fig. 95) is usually seen on the ground near stream banks.

Food is also a kind of resource that snakes divide. The reed snakes are earthworm specialists; that is the fixed diet of all 19 species known from Sabah. The slug-eating snakes *(Pareas)* and the smooth snakes *(Liopeltis)* also feed on invertebrates. However, the vast majority of Sabah's snakes feed on vertebrates, with frogs and lizards being the common prey for the most species. Mammals and birds are the usual food of a few snakes, including the reticulated python and the dog-toothed cat snake (*Boiga cynodon* (Fig. 94). The cat snake, often reaching more than 2 m in length, has very long teeth which may be an adaptation for feeding on birds; long teeth would surely enable it to penetrate feathers and get a firm grip on its prey.

Both tadpoles and adult frogs may evolve into habitat specialists. Since these hilly forests have such a variety of streams, they provide the maximum opportunity for tadpoles to specialize in terms of microhabitats. This may explain why frogs reach their greatest species diversity in these hilly forests. Of the roughly 50% of Bornean frogs that breed at streams, some do so mainly at small streams about 1–2 m wide (for example, Kuhl's creek frog, *Rana kuhli*, Fig. 99), others at slightly wider (4–6 m) creeks, and others mainly at larger streams. Some frog species breed only along relatively gently flowing creeks and others require stronger currents.

Tadpoles also sort out differences among different parts of a stream. For example, tadpoles of the white-lipped frog *(Rana chalconota)* stick to quiet, shallow pools at the edge of a stream. Tadpoles of Blyth's frog *(Rana blythi),* the spotted stream frog *(Rana signata),* and the brown slender toad *(Ansonia leptopus,* Fig. 100) live mainly in clumps of dead leaves that accumulate on creek beds wherever eddy currents develop. In shallow riffles over sand and gravel, the typical tadpoles are those of the slender litter frog, *Leptolalax dringi* (Fig. 97), and the short-nosed tree frog, *Rhacophorus gauni* (Fig. 98). The tadpoles of the litter frog are unusually slender which enables them to wriggle down into the crevices between pieces of gravel on the bottom where they feed on bits of dead leaves that become wedged in these spaces. Gravel and sand riffles in

Fig. 97. (Left) *Leptolalax dringi*, slender litter frog. *(Photo: C.L. Chan)*

Fig. 98. (Above) *Rhacophorus gauni*, short-nosed tree frog. *(Photo: R.F. Inger)*

Fig. 99. *Rana kuhli,* Kuhl's creek frog. *(Photo: R.F. Inger)*

Fig. 100. *Ansonia leptopus,* brown slender toad. *(Photo: R.F. Inger)*

small streams are also the home of larvae of caecilians (Fig. 10), the elongated worm-like amphibians; they, too, force their way into tight spaces in the bottom.

Another group of tadpoles, the larvae of species of torrent frogs (genus *Meristogenys* Fig. 101) and some of the slender toads (genus *Ansonia* Fig. 102), live in strong rapids on clear, swift, rocky streams. They cling

Fig. 101. (Above) *Meristogenys orphnocnemis,* Sabah torrent frog. *(Photo: R.F. Inger)*

Fig. 102. (Right) *Ansonia spinulifer,* spiny slender toad. *(Photo: R.F. Inger)*

Fig. 103. *Rana palavanensis,* smooth guardian frog. *(Photo: R.F. Inger)*

to rocks in the strongest currents, in the case of torrent frog tadpoles, by means of a sucker on the underside of the body or, in the case of the slender toads, by means of wide, cup-like lips. If they are disturbed, they simply release their hold and let the current carry them to another rock to which they attach. When undisturbed, they move slowly over the surface scraping minute algae that grow on the rock. At night, *Meristogenys* tadpoles often form aggregations of 25 to 100 individuals on the top of a rock and may even be largely out of water. The function of this behaviour remains a mystery. Is it a response to change in barometric pressure? An approaching storm?

In areas where the ground is not too steep, depressions collect rain water and these pools are used by the same species of frogs that breed in similar sites in flat forests (p. 36). To the pond breeders mentioned earlier, we need to add the smooth guardian frog, *Rana palavanensis* (Fig. 103). Males of this remarkable frog call from under or on dead leaves on the forest floor at some distance from any body of water; the female finds the male by tracing the call and lays her eggs usually under a dead leaf at the male's calling station. The male remains with the eggs, presumably guarding them from insect predators; when the tadpoles hatch they somehow manage to climb on to the back of the male, which then hops off into a small rain pool where the tadpoles swim away to complete their development.

Where the hills are very steep, as in the Crocker Range of western Sabah, there are very few ponds in the forest. So in forests in this topography the usual pond-breeding tree frogs are scarce. But that does affect the species that breed in tree holes, such as the brilliantly patterned cinnamon tree frog, *Nyctixalus pictus* (Fig. 105). The tadpoles of this species can develop successfully in water containing tree holes, in cavities of logs, and even in large, hollow fruit, so that steepness of the terrain does not affect the ability of this species to reproduce.

Turtles also find a variety of habitats in the lowland forest. Small to medium-sized creeks with gravel and rock bottoms provide home to two very different kinds of turtles, the high-shelled creek terrapin *Notochelys platynota* (Fig. 104) and the flat dwarf soft-shelled turtle *Dogania subplana*. Neither of these species leaves water except to lay eggs. The creek terrapin starts out life feeding on a mixture of insects, other invertebrates, and soft plants. As it grows, the proportion of vegetation in the diet increases until as an adult it is completely herbivorous. It is actually rather common in hilly forest streams, but is not often seen because it remains in water. The dwarf soft-shelled turtle is encountered more often because as a juvenile it favours shallow sandy or gravel-bottomed creeks where its four to six large black spots stand out. Young individuals feed mainly on aqautic insects and small crabs. Not much is known about the diet of large adults (shell length 20–25 cm), but they probably eat larger crabs, snails, and perhaps small fish. Larger rivers are the home of the common Malaysian soft-shelled turtle *Amyda cartilaginea*, a large species reaching lengths of over 50 cm. Fishermen often catch individuals weighing more than 5 kilograms on hook-and-

Fig. 104. (Right) *Notochelys platynota*, creek terrapin. *(Photo: W.M. Poon)*

Fig. 105. (Above) *Nyctixalus pictus,* cinnamon tree frog. *(Photo: C.L. Chan)*

line baited with fish. It has a nasty disposition and needs to be handled with respect.

Away in the forest, the two species we have seen most often are the large Asian brown tortoise *Manouria emys* and the spiny terrapin *Heosemys spinosa* (Fig. 106). Both are mainly vegetarians, eating fallen fruits and soft vegetation. We have never seen these species walking across the forest floor, but have always found them in "forms", the slight, shell-sized depressions a turtle makes in the floor litter. The brown tortoise, a typical high-domed terrestrial turtle, is quite large, reaching a shell length up to 50 cm. The spiny terrapin is called as such because each marginal scale of its upper shell ends in a sharp, projecting point, it has a flatter shell than the brown tortoise and is only half the size. Some observers of this species say it spends much time in creeks, but we have seen it only on land.

Fig. 106. *Heosemys spinosa,* spiny terrapin. *(Photo: W.M. Poon)*

CHAPTER 5

AMPHIBIANS AND REPTILES
OF SUBMONTANE AND
MONTANE ZONES

Along the mountainous spine of Sabah, from Kinabalu south along the Crocker Range to Mount Lumaku, the lowland dipterocarp forests give way at about 1000–1200 metres to montane forests in which oaks, chestnuts, coniferous trees, and tree ferns predominate (Fig. 107). These forests seem darker than the lowland hill forests, probably because of the mists that shroud them so much of the time.

For amphibians and reptiles, cold-blooded animals, the climate at the higher elevations of the montane zone becomes a critical environmental factor. As everyone knows, it is cooler in the mountains than near sea

Fig. 107. Oak-chestnut forest on Mount Kinabalu. *(Photo: R.F. Inger)*

level. The average daily temperature drops about 4°C (7°F) with every 1000 metre increase in elevation. What also changes is the amount of cloudiness. As the sun climbs, it heats up vegetation causing evaporation of water from leaves. Commonly that moisture condenses in the cool early morning air in lowland forests forming ground mist. As the temperature rises during the morning, that lowland ground mist disappears and the moisture rises and condenses into clouds and swirling mist as passes into the cooler air at higher elevation. This is why the crown of Kinabalu (Fig. 108) is so often hidden and why we are urged to reach the peak by dawn if we want a clear view of the land below.

Relatively few of Sabah's lizards, and snakes can tolerate the cool temperatures that prevail above 850 m. In general, the physiology of these animals simply does not function well in montane temperatures. Frogs seem to be less affected by low temperatures than the reptiles. Of course, it is possible for a lizard or snake to move into a sun spot on the forest floor and gain some heat for its body. But few of them do. In fact, the cloudy conditions common in the mountains limit the opportunities

to bask in the warmth of the sun. It is striking that the sun basking brown skinks *(Mabuya),* which are so abundant in the lowlands, are very rare in these montane forests.

The steep topography of the mountains has another effect on environment that is particularly important for Sabah's frog fauna. Streams at high elevations are usually small because their drainage basins are small, and they always have strong currents. About half of the species

Fig. 108. Montane forest with peaks of Kinabalu. *(Photo: C.M. Clarke)*

Fig. 109. Steep rocky stream at 650–750 metres above sea level. *(Photo: R.F. Inger)*

of Bornean frogs breed in streams, and about half of those breed in slowly flowing or almost standing water—in places such as quiet side pools. Species with those requirements have small chance of finding a suitable place to lay eggs and have their tadpoles complete development in montane forests. The many species of Bornean frog that breed in small ponds would also have a difficult time finding good breeding sites at high elevations because ponds rarely develop in the steep topography.

The unfavourable montane environment leads to a reduction in the total number of amphibians and reptiles that live at high elevations. On Mount Kinabalu below 1000 m a total of 48 species of frogs has been recorded, but only 33 species above that. A small toad holds the highest record for an amphibian on Kinabalu—at 3100 metres. The reptiles of Kinabalu are much less well known. On the lower slopes of Mount Kinabalu, between 200 and 600 metres above sea level, we have seen 17 species of lizards and 23 species of snakes. From Park Headquarters at 1500 metres to 3000 metres, we have recorded only six species of lizards and 13 species of snakes. The highest observation point for a reptile on Kinabalu is for a snake, *Rhabdophis murudensis,* at 2200 metres. One word of caution here: We think the list of reptiles known from Kinabalu, at all elevations, is certain to grow as more research is carried on by Sabah Parks.

At the south end of the Crocker Range, at Mount Lumaku, the same pattern of more species below the montane zone than in it is repeated. We worked at elevations between 650 metres, where hill diptercarp forests with huge buttressed trees are common, to 1350 metres, where the montane oak-chestnut forest takes over. Even at 650 metres the terrain is very steep so that streams are rocky and swift (Fig. 109), just

Fig. 110. *Philautus aurantium,* golden-legged bush frog. *(Photo: R.F. Inger)*

Fig. 111. *Philautus bunitus,* mountain bush frog. *(Photo: R.F. Inger)*

as they are at 1200 metres. Still the slight change in environment over a matter of 400–500 metres has an effect on the fauna. We saw 48 species of frogs, 16 species of lizards, 20 species of snakes, and two turtles below 800 metres, but only 32 species of frogs, nine of lizards, seven of snakes, but no turtles above 1000 metres. Two of the bush frogs *(Philautus)* we saw at 1150–1350 metres were new species (Figs. 110–111).

There are a few montane specialists, species that have become adapted to the environment and are mainly restricted to these high elevations. As is often the case, environmental conditions that are bad for some species are favourable for others. The clouds that contribute to cool, unfavourable conditions for some amphibians and reptiles promote the development of thick layers of wet, almost soggy moss on the ground, on rotting logs, and even on tree trunks. One group of frogs, the small bush frogs (genus *Philautus*, Fig. 112), utilize this mossy blanket as the place to lay their eggs. The bush frogs have an unfrog-like life cycle. Instead of laying a large number of small eggs, they lay a very small number (about 10–12) of very large eggs (about 0.3 cm in a female about 2 cm long). The eggs are laid, not in water as in the case of a "normal"

Fig. 112. *Philautus ingeri,* sharp-nosed bush frog. *(Photo: R.F. Inger)*

Fig. 113. (Right) *Rhacophorus baluensis,* Kinabalu tree frog. *(Photo: R.F. Inger)*

Fig. 114. *Rhacophorus everetti,* mossy tree frog. *(Photo: R.F. Inger)*

frog, but in a moist area such as in moss covering a log or under dead leaves on the forest floor. Then, instead of hatching into free swimming tadpoles, the young develop within the gelatinous egg envelope and hatch as tiny froglets. One indication of the success of the bush frogs in this montane environment is the fact that they constitute 30% of the species of frogs that live in Bornean montane forests.

Other frogs make a living in these forests. When the mossy tree frog, *Rhacophorus everetti* (Fig. 114) sits on a moss-covered log, its mottled green and brown pattern and its rough skin combine to give a remarkable camouflage. Only when it comes to breed along streams and climbs on smooth leaves is it easily visible. A second species of these montane frogs, the Kinabalu tree frog, *Rhacophorus baluensis* (Fig. 113), breeds at small ponds and seems to survive even rather severe environmental disturbance; as long as clumps of small trees and shrubs persist, this frog does too.

Just below the mossy cloud forest, but still in the montane oak-conifer forest, is the home of a short, fat snake, *Oreocalamus hanitschi* (Fig. 115), which lives under rocks and seems to feed mainly on earthworms. For 75 years, this snake was known only from Mount Kinabalu. But

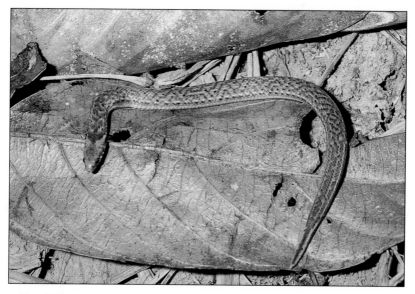

Fig. 115. *Oreocalamus hanitschi,* mountain reed snake. *(Photo: R.F. Inger)*

69

Fig. 116. *Phoxophrys cephalum,* a spiny-tailed agamid. *(Photo: R.F. Inger)*

since it has recently been found at Lumaku and just to the south in the highlands of northern Sarawak, it must occur in the mountains throughout Borneo. Our knowledge of other snakes is also improving and one that was originally discovered in lowlands in Sarawak, the Bornean flat-headed snake, *Stegonotus borneensis,* seems to live mainly in this montane zone; most of the known specimens have been found above 1200 metres in Sabah, mainly around the headquarters of Kinabalu Park. A third montane snake, a small reed snake, *Calamaria griswoldi,* was discovered first 70 years ago on Mount Kinabalu and thought to be rare; but many specimens have been found by Sabah Parks staff on the road around the park headquarters.

The same oak-conifer forest provides a home for a few lizards not found elsewhere. Two small slender skinks, *Sphenomorphus kinabaluensis* and an undescribed new species, move about in the litter of the forest floor. The new species, only 3–4 cm long, is quite abundant in the oak forest of Mount Lumaku. At least one forest gecko, the Kinabalu bent-toed gecko *Gonydactylus baluensis* (Figs. 117–118), is abundant throughout the montane oak forest of western Sabah. Since geckos are normally active at night when tempreatures are relatively low, the montane climate poses no problem for this species. Two other lizards that live in this

Fig. 118. (right) Eye of *Gonydactylus baluensis.* As the three pin-hole openings in the contracted iris focus on a single spot of the retina, geckos of this genus are able to take in more light without giving up the sharp focus provided by the pin hole opening. *(Photo: C.L. Chan)*

Fig. 117. (Above) *Gonydactylus baluensis,* Kinabalu angle-toed gecko. *(Photo: C.L. Chan)*

forest, both species of the genus *Phoxophrys* (Fig. 116) are members of the agamid family. Little is known about their natural history, but adult males have spiny tails with swollen bases and bulging muscles at the rear of the head, suggesting that they probably fight for territories or mates. We have found them only on the ground though they probably climb in low vegetation. Arboreal lizards active during the day are essentially absent in these montane forests. No one has ever seen flying lizards *(Draco)* in oak-conifer forests; probably the frequent mists do not allow them enough time to bask in the sun and warm up to their normal operating temperatures.

There is another kind of specialist, frogs that breed in swift, rocky streams, that does well in montane forests. These frogs are members of three genera and three families. Two species of torrent frogs (genus *Meristogenys,* Fig. 119) and four species of slender toads (genus *Ansonia,* Fig. 121) live along tumbling mountain creeks. One of the things these genera have in common is that their tadpoles have a sucker device that allows them to cling to rocks in strong currents; they can sometimes be seen during the day through the clear water plastered against rocks. In the case of *Ansonia* the sucker is formed by the

Fig. 119. *Meristogenys kinabaluensis,* mountain torrent frog. *(Photo: R.F. Inger)*

72

Fig. 120. (Left) *Rhacophorus angulirostris,* sharp-nosed tree frog. *(Photo: R.B. Stuebing)*

tadpole's expanded lips and in the case of *Meristogenys* tadpoles the entire belly forms the sucker. One species of tree frog, *Rhacophorus angulirostris* (Fig. 120), the sharp-nosed tree frog, is the representative of the third genus and family mentioned. Adults of this tree frog wander freely through the oak-conifer forest, but come to streams to breed. Their tadpoles do not cling to the surface of rocks, but instead wriggle into crevices on the bottom. As each of these genera has a number of species living in hilly lowland forests, all with the same general habits, most likely the montane species are the only ones

Fig. 121. (Below) *Ansonia hanitschi,* Hanitsch's slender toad. *(Photo: R.F. Inger)*

Fig. 122. *Leptobrachium montanum,* mountain litter frog. *(Photo: C.L. Chan)*

that have adapted to the cool temper-atures of high elevations. That kind of evolutionary adjustment is probably the explanation for the separ-ation of the mountain litter frog *Leptobrachium montanum* (Fig. 122) from its lowland relatives.

Given the environmental conditions in montane forests it is surprising to see a few typical lowland species doing well. Kuhl's creek frog (*Rana kuhli,* Fig. 99) is the best example among frogs. It is quite abundant in small creeks at the level of Kinabalu Park Headquarters (about 1600 metres). We are not certain how its tadpoles survive the force of current in these steep gradient streams during run-off after rains. They have no obvious adaptation to strong currents; most likely they take shelter in eddy currents around large rocks in the beds of the streams. At any rate, the ability of this species to survive from near sea level to almost 2000 metres suggests remarkable adaptability. This quality may explain the extremely broad geographic range of the species: from southern China and Burma to Sumatra, Borneo, and Java. The Sarawak keelback snake, *Rhabdophis sarawakensis* and the Sumatran pit-viper, *Trimeresurus sumatranus,* are the only snakes in Borneo that can match the altitudinal range of *Rana kuhli.* Neither of these snakes, however, can match the distribution of *Rana kuhli;* they occur in Sumatra but, on the continent of Asia, are not found beyond southern Thailand.

Biologists from many countries have visited Mount Kinabalu to study amphibians and reptiles mainly because mountains, especially isolated ones, tend to have species unique to them. All the species mentioned in this chapter with the names *"baluensis"* or *"kinabaluensis"* are the product of that attention. For years, before biological exploration in Borneo became more systematic, scientists thought those species occurred nowhere else. Isolated mountains are like islands surrounded by a "sea" of lowlands with a different climate. However, we now know that many of those species are rather widely distributed in Bornean mountains; the mountain reed snake *(Oreocalamus hanitschi)* mentioned above is a good example. The mountain torrent frog *(Meristogenys kinabaluensis)* and the mountain dwarf litter frog *(Leptobrachella baluensis)* are now known to occur from Kinabalu at least as far as Mount Mulu in northern Sarawak despite any lowland gaps. The explanation for these distributions across lowland gaps is rather simple. During the ice ages that covered northern Eurasia and North America with glaciers, average temperatures dropped even in the tropics, bringing the climate that is now found only above, say, 1200 metre, down to 500–600 metres. Consequently, a "montane" climate formed a continuous belt without gaps and allowed montane species to spread from whichever place they orginated. When the earth's climate warmed, the montane climate retreated up the mountains and so did the montane species.

CHAPTER 6

MAN CREATES HOMES FOR AMPHIBIANS AND REPTILES

When we clear land for a rice field or construct a road to connect village and town or build a house, we rarely think of those activities as building homes for a variety of other creatures. But in effect that is exactly what we are doing inadvertently. In fact, without our work at changing environments, quite a few species of frogs and reptiles would not be in Sabah or anywhere else in Borneo. This phenomenon is not unique to Borneo, but is repeated all over the tropics.

First, let us consider the physical environment we create in Sabah. When we build a village or a housing estate or create padi fields, besides removing the forest, we make new climates. Immediately the maximum daily temperature increases and so the difference between day and night temperature increases. In an open town center or at the edge of a padi field, on a sunny day the temperature commonly rises to 33°–35°C (91°–95°F) in mid-afternoon from night-time lows of 21°–22°C (70°–72°F) (Fig. 123). On the other hand, in a lowland rain forest the daily range is normally from 22°–23°C (72°–74°F) to 28°–30°C (82°–86°F). The increase in the amount of sunshine results in faster drying of small pools of rain water. These changes can make it impossible for many rain forest species to exist. Most reptiles are very sensitive to high temperatures; direct exposure to sunshine can kill a snake in a few minutes. Rapid drying of rain pools can lead to the death of an entire clutch of rain forest tadpoles which usually take several weeks to complete development.

On the positive side, when we make a flooded rice field or a ditch to drain a road, we are also making a fine breeding place for frogs and, therefore, a place where some snakes can find a lot of prey. These are also good environments for the Malayan box turtle *Cuora amboinensis* (Fig. 51), which then turns up commonly in town markets. Also some our domesticated animals make positive contributions to wildlife in ways we

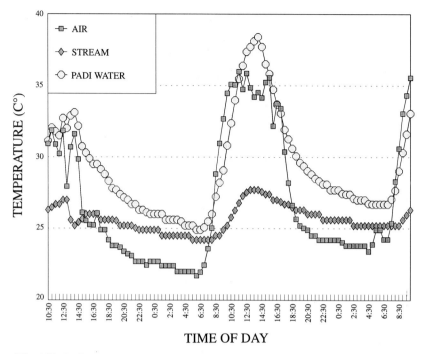

Fig. 123. Daily temperature rhythm of air and water at a rice field compared to air temperature at a stream flowing through tree cover. *(Courtesy of Dr. H.K. Voris and Dr. D. Karns).*

Fig. 124. *Varanus salvator,* biawak, or monitor lizard. *(Photo: C.L. Chan)*

have not exactly planned. Water buffalo make wallows that are frog heaven, and the crabs that are attracted to the wallows provide food for certain kinds of snakes. Chickens make another kind of contribution that no farmer is happy about; there is nothing a monitor lizard (*Varanus salvator,* Fig. 124) or a python likes more than a tasty meal of chicken.

The amphibian and reptile fauna of agricultural fields, villages, and towns is not just a reduced version of the rain forest fauna. Instead it is a very different fauna consisting mainly of specialists that are associated with humans all through southern Asia and adjacent islands. In fact, most of them seem to require man to open up or clear forests before they can find suitable habitat and they seem unable to invade the rain forest. The list of these species in Sabah is impressive: at least seven species of frogs, six species of lizards, and one snake. Furthermore, some of them apparently have used us to carry them from one land mass to another, although that certainly was not our intention in the majority of species. Only one of these "weed species"— we give these specialists that name because like plant weeds they thrive wherever man has seriously disturbed natural environments—is a known case of deliberate introduction by man. The Taiwanese frog, *Rana rugulosa,* was introduced as a new crop for sale in markets about ten years ago. As might have been expected, it has escaped confinement and is now common in ponds and low places at least around Kota Kinabalu.

These "weedy" species have certain qualities that adapt them to the environments we create. The lizards generally have reproductive characteristics that simplify transportation and the start of a new colony. For example, the village brown skink, *Mabuya multifasciata* (Fig. 125) is a live bearer which enables a single gravid female to start a colony. All the house geckos, for example, *Hemidactylus frenatus* (Fig. 126) or *Gehyra mutilata* have hard-shelled eggs that adhere to backs of pictures or to a plank and require several weeks to incubate; that is enough time for a piece of furniture with its attached gecko eggs to be moved considerable distance and set the stage for a new colony of geckos.

All the weed species of frogs and reptiles have to tolerate higher extremes of temperatures than their rain forest relatives. In the case of the amphibians this tolerance involves both adult frogs and tadpoles. We have watched a pair of mating four-lined tree frogs (*Polypedates leucomystax,* Fig. 127), in full sun at the edge of a water-filled road rut, remain in that position for two and one-half hours. They clearly were able to withstand the high body heat produced by that exposure, but they also had either to prevent or tolerate loss

Fig. 125. *Mabuya multifasciata,* village brown skink. *(Photo: R.F. Inger)*

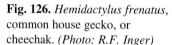

Fig. 126. *Hemidactylus frenatus,* common house gecko, or cheechak. *(Photo: R.F. Inger)*

of body fluids. Probably no rain forest frog could have matched that endurance.

We have also observed tadpoles of the four-lined tree frog living in small pools exposed to full sunlight with water temperatures of 38°–40°C, about 15°–17° higher than the temperatures in most rain forest pools. Water at that high temperature cannot hold much oxygen in solution, which would impose another strain on some kinds of tadpoles.

In effect, through our normal economic activities we make a variety of habitats for amphibians and reptiles unintentionally. Houses, whether in towns or in small villages, are quickly occupied not just by people but by a variety of house geckos. One of them, the common cheechak *Hemidactylus frenatus* (Fig. 126), is such a good traveler that it now occurs in warm climates in many parts of the world. Three species of house geckos in Sabah, all about 10–12 cm long, are such common parts of a home environment for those of us who live in Sabah that we no longer notice them as they chirp and scamper across ceilings and walls at night feeding on the insects attracted to the lights. But even these geckos have slight specializations in their selection of places to live within our communities. A study of these species by a student at Universiti Kebangsaan Malaysia (Sabah), Yong Chuan Siew, shows that the round-tailed gecko, *Gehyra mutilata,* lives mainly on the outside of wooden buildings on the outskirts of towns, in contrast to the flat-tailed gecko, *Platyurus platyurus,* which is seen mostly on the outer walls of cement buildings near town centres. The common house gecko, or cheechak as is is known locally, is the species most often seen inside buildings and shows a preference for wooden houses, but does not seem to care whether it lives in town or not.

Fig. 127. *Polypedates leucomystax,* four-lined tree frog. *(Photo: C.L. Chan)*

Fig. 128. *Bronchocoela cristatella,* green tree lizard. *(Photo: C.L. Chan)*

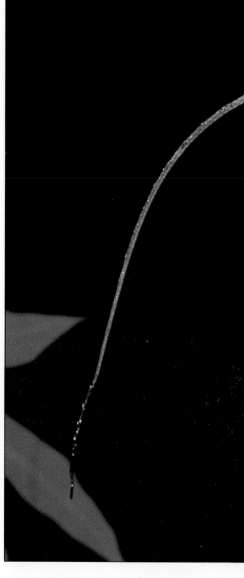

All of these geckos, like most reptiles associated with man, are found over very large parts of Southeast Asia and even beyond. But nature is full of surprises. Eight years ago two Japanese biologists described a new species of house gecko, *Lepidodactylus ranauensis,* that they caught on the wall of a coffee-shop in Ranau. It has not been found anywhere else since then.

Gardens around houses with shrubs and trees, especially those near secondary growth at the edge of town, are likely to have a mixture of genuine rain forest species. A few rain forest lizards that are mostly active up in the forest canopy, where the temperature usually reaches the levels it does in towns (about 30°–33°C, or 86°–91°F), find suitable habitats in town gardens. The green tree lizard *Bronchocoela cristatella* (Fig. 128) is occasionally seen in gardens. If a home garden is near a marshy area, several forest frogs, for example, the saffron-bellied frog (*Chaperina fusca,* Fig. 64) or the greater swamp frog (*Rana ingeri,* Fig. 75) may wander in.

Every town in Sabah has flat areas—at least a football field—that flood after a heavy rain. The flooding is followed at night by a noisy chorus of frog calls produced by at least five species of frogs. The loudest members of the chorus are the banded bullfrogs, *Kaloula pulchra* (Fig. 129), with the

82

Taiwanese frog *Rana rugulosa* a close second. They are joined by the grass frog *Rana limnocharis,* the cricket frog *Rana nicobariensis,* and the four-lined tree frog *Polypedates leucomystax* (Fig.127). Roadside ditches attract some of the same species, particularly the cricket frog, which often calls even in the absence of rain.

Fig. 129. *Kaloula pulchra,* banded bullfrog. *(Photo: C.L. Chan)*

Flooded rice fields are an even better place for frogs. In Sabah, as in most of South East Asia, the most abundant species is the green paddy frog, *Rana erythraea* (Fig. 130). No one has tried to estimate the number of paddy frogs in a rice field, but they must number in the thousands. Other species commonly found are the grass frog and the cricket frog. Frogs are an important part of the economics of rice production. Someone once calculated that in a hectare of rice fields the frogs save 1000 kilos of vegetation by eating insects that feed on plants.

An ever increasing type of man-made habitat are tree plantations—oil palm, cocoa, coffee, rubber. These tree plantation with their dense shade develop climates much more like genuine forests than other environments we create. In theory at least, the plantations could attract a wide variety of forest reptiles, except for the heavy application of pesticides. Unfortunately, we have very little information on the amount and variety of amphibians and reptiles among the oil palm or cocoa trees. We will need that kind of information if we are to have a better understanding of conservation of amphibians and reptiles in a developing tropical economy.

Fig. 130. *Rana erythraea,* green paddy frog. *(Photo: R.F. Inger)*

CHAPTER 7

CONSERVING SABAH'S AMPHIBIANS AND REPTILES

L ike biologists and non-scientists with an interest in the world around us, we are concerned though not yet desperate about the conservation of Sabah's amphibians and reptiles. A sceptical, thoughtful person might ask, "Why?" Part of our answer would be that this array of beautifully coloured animals with their variety of sizes, shapes, behaviour, and habitat specializations represents a portion of the natural treasure of Sabah. Our sceptical friend might still ask, "But why amphibians and reptiles?" It is true that butterflies and birds, dragonflies and beetles, trees and orchids are equally important parts of that natural treasure. But we know about amphibians and reptiles and are better prepared to talk about them. Furthermore, since conserving these creatures is likely to result in conservation of all these riches, by arguing for conservation of amphibians and reptiles we are also arguing for conservation of all.

As we discuss conservation, we need to separate the species of the forests, that is, the original, native fauna of Sabah, from the species that have recently arrived to live with and around man. The native fauna is much richer and is also much more distinctive, that is, many of the species are found only in Borneo. The "weedy" species that live with man and depend upon human activities are few in number, not very colourful, and live throughout Southeast Asia; there is nothing distinctly "Bornean" about them and most of the actions that harm the native species will not harm these newcomers. For these reasons, we will concentrate our attention on conservation of the native species.

Severe habitat disturbance and disappearance are the main dangers to plant and animal species around the world. The same, of course, holds true in Sabah. That kind of disturbance may be chemical (for example, chemical pollution) or physical (for example, clearing a forest). It may also be climatic. All of these kinds of changes have occurred as part of natural phenomena in the past. For example, very heavy rains have caused large landslides that have removed chunks of forest. Volcanoes have erupted and shed quantities of acidic ash in rivers. Climates changed during the glacial periods. When such events occurred naturally in the past, there was always the opportunity for species either to adapt to changes or to reinvade the damaged areas slowly from adjacent havens. Now, however, the changes occur so rapidly or with such frequency or over such wide areas that adaptation is impossible and immigration from surrounding environments not likely. And that is one reason why we think we should be concerned.

"Well," says our sceptical friend, "suppose I am content to lose these interesting creatures in exchange for clear economic benefits. Why should I be worried about those animals?" Because, we reply, some of the major things that affect them adversely also affect us in the same way; the economic gains are not as clear or as simple as we thought. Consider that removing forest cover, which has a detrimental effect on rain forest species, means that the vegetation and land do not hold rain when it falls, leading to rapid runoff locally and to flooding downstream. Local papers are filled with stories about flooding in towns after even moderately heavy rain. Such floods will be more frequent and widespread as we remove more of the forest. Someone will have to pay for the damage. In the paragraphs that follow, the implications for the quality of human life should be obvious.

The main, clearly visible sources of problems for the native fauna of Sabah are logging and agriculture. Both affect forest cover and water quality in streams and both affect large portions of the state. However, the ways they affect the lives of amphibians and reptiles are complex and varied. Traditionally, agriculture in Sabah has involved clearing a small tract of forest, burning the logs and debris as soon as they dried, and then planting the crop in the newly created open field. All the frogs, lizards, and snakes that depended on the trees for perch and resting sites were left homeless and all those that depended on the leaf litter and normal dead logs for resting and hunting areas were, of course, displaced and many of them died because of exposure to intense sunshine and lack of proper prey. In the past, these cleared areas were abandoned after a few years and allowed to regenerate secondary growth forest.

But agriculture has changed greatly in Sabah in recent years. Although shifting agriculture, or the cutting and burning of forest still goes on, fields tend to be used for a number of years. There are large tracts of commercial vegetable gardening, especially on the slopes of Kinabalu (outside the Kinabalu Park) but elsewhere also. These new types of farms rely heavily on use of pesticides and commercial fertilizers. The rainy climate typical of these farming areas is supplemented by irrigation. Runoff inevitably carries both classes of chemicals into streams. There have been few studies on the effects of these chemicals on aquatic life in Sabah and we know of none on tadpoles specifically. However, studies in other parts of the world have shown that aquatic life is adversely affected both by pesticides and fertilizers from farmland. At best, the pesticides can't be good for tadpoles or any other animals. We are certainly not the only persons who always wash the vegetables we buy to get rid of the chemicals.

Plantations of trees—oil palm, rubber, etc.—have some of the superficial attributes of forests. Shade is dense, humidity should be high, and temperatures should not fluctuate very much. Those features should enable them to support a good fauna of amphibians and reptiles. On the other hand, use of chemicals in these plantations is often high and there is necessarily a lot of human activity in them. In fact no one has made a study of amphibians and reptiles in these plantations and, until some one does, we will have no idea what their fauna is.

Selective logging has some of the same effects as land clearing for agricultural purposes. Logging also destroys some resting sites of forest species and changes the climate within a forest as it becomes more open and as the sun reaches the ground with less obstruction. Usually commercial logging requires the building of many roads into an area of forest for heavy equipment. These roads become major sources for silt that is flushed into rivers with each rain. Clear streams are changed into muddy ones. Although even streams flowing through primary, undisturbed forest carry loads of silt after heavy storms, a recent study has revealed dramatic differences between these forest streams and those flowing through recently logged forests. The streams in unlogged areas clear after a few hours, and in a short while one can once more see the bare gravel and rocks on the bottom. In contrast, streams flowing through recently logged forest carry about ten times the amount of silt after a storm and are always cloudy with a heavy, perpetual coat of silt on the bottom. This bottom coating of mud eliminates the food supply of several groups of tadpoles (mainly those of the torrent frogs, *Meristogenys,* and the slender toads, *Ansonia*) that cling to rocks in clear water and scrape the algae that grow on those rocks. Without survival of tadpoles, populations of these frogs cannot persist for long.

However, the picture is not simply black and white, as was proven to us by our experience on the slopes of Mount Lumaku in southwestern Sabah. We worked there in two kinds of situations. One was an area that had been selectively logged three to five years before we arrived and had been left undisturbed afterwards. Although this forest had obviously been severely damaged, there were still some large trees, very heavy undergrowth, and the rocky streams ran clear and swift. The other area only five kilometres away had been almost clear cut, only a few shrubs remained, and the stream we worked in was cloudy and had a layer of silt over the bottom. The "old" logged forest had a fauna of amphibians and reptiles as rich as any in undisturbed rain forest and the clear, rocky stream had as many torrent frog tadpoles as we have seen anywhere. In contrast, we found almost no amphibians and reptiles in the other, newly logged area; we found a few adult torrent frogs along the silty stream, but no tadpoles. Apparently, if the logging is limited to the usual selective style and if the forest is then left alone, natural regeneration of vegetation is fast enough to tie down the soil in a few years and restore the environment to the essentials needed by many species of rain forest amphibians and reptiles.

The same seems to be true of old abandoned sites of shifting agriculture. We worked at one place near Kota Marudu in northern Sabah that had been clear cut, we were told, for hill rice cultivation and then abandoned 50 years before our visit. The amphibians and reptiles were as diverse and as abundant there as in any good rain forest. However, two points must be mentioned. The place had been left undisturbed all that time. Secondly, it was next to the northern boundary of Kinabalu Park, so that forest species could invade a regenerating forest. Obviously, these were especially favourable conditions.

The amount of forested area in Sabah is certain to shrink permanently as the human population grows and as economic development proceeds. This process is bound to affect the amphibian and reptile fauna adversely. Because natural populations fluctuate in size in the absence of outside disturbance, the local populations of some species will die out and not be replaced as forest areas become permanently separated. The consequence is that the number of species living in any one patch of forest will decrease over time.

Nevertheless, from the standpoint of conservation of amphibians and reptiles (and all other biota), Sabah is better off than most tropical countries and that is due largely to its park system. Sabah Parks are well-regarded by the public, they are well-guarded, and best of all they include large areas of primary rain forest well-distributed over the state and over all elevations from lowland to treeline on Mount Kinabalu. The Danum Valley Conservation Area on the east side of Sabah protects another large area of primary rain forest and all its species. Governmental actions are supplemented by several citizens' conservation organizations. Especially notable are the Malaysian Nature Society (Sabah Branch), the Sabah Society and the Sabah Zoological Society. These societies have broad conservation interests, covering all groups of plants and animals.

Our conclusions are that Sabah overall still has a very rich fauna of amphibians and reptiles, that there are still areas in Sabah, particularly in the parks, where many species of these animals maintain healthy populations, and that the actions we take that are detrimental to these animals carry with them costs to us as well. While the climate for conservation in Sabah is favourable now, the lesson from other parts of the world is that without interested and concerned citizens that climate can change.

REFERENCES

Berry, P.Y. 1975. *The Amphibian Fauna of Peninsular Malaysia.* Tropical Press, Kuala Lumpur. x + 130 pp.

Campbell, E.J.F. 1994. *A Walk through the Lowland Rain Forest of Sabah.* Natural History Publications (Borneo) Sdn. Bhd., Kota Kinabalu. viii + 83 pp.

Haile, N.S. 1958. *The Snakes of Borneo, with a Key to the Species.* *Sarawak Museum Journal* 8: 743–771.

Inger, R.F. 1990. *The Systematics and Zoogeography of the Amphibia of Borneo. Fieldiana: Zoology* 52: 1–402. (2nd printing)

Inger, R.F. & R.B. Stuebing. 1989. *Frogs of Sabah.* Sabah Parks Publication no. 10. Sabah Parks Trustees, Kota Kinabalu. iv + 133 pp.

Inger, R.F. & R.B. Stuebing. 1992. *The Montane Amphibian fauna of Northwestern Borneo. Malayan Nature Journal* 46: 1–51.

Inger, R.F., R.B. Stuebing & Tan Fui Lian. 1995. *New species and new records of Anurans from Borneo.* The Raffles Bulletin of Zoology (Singapore) 43(1): 115–131.

Kiew, B.H. 1983. *Key to Malaysian Snake.* Jabatan Zoologi, Universiti Malaya, Kuala Lumpur 1–14.

Kiew, B.H. 1984. *Conservation Status of the Malaysian Fauna. IV. Reptiles. Malayan Naturalist* 38(2): 2–3

Luping, M., Chin Wen & E.R. Dingley (eds.) 1978. *Kinabalu—Summit of Borneo.* Sabah Society Monograph. The Sabah Society, Kota Kinabalu. 486 pp.

Lim, B.L. 1991. *Poisonous Snakes of Peninsular Malaysia.* Malayan Nature Society, Kuala Lumpur. 8 + 74 pp. (Third edition)

Lim, F.L.K. & M.T.M. Lee. 1989. *Fascinating Snakes of Southeast Asia—An Introduction.* Tropical Press, Kuala Lumpur. xv + 124 pp.

Stuebing, R.B. 1991. *A Checklist of the Snakes of Borneo.* Raffles Bulletin of Zoology (Singapore) 39: 323–362.

Stuebing, R.B., Engkamat Lading & Francis S.P. Liew. 1990. *Snake Island of Pulau Tiga Park.* Sabah Parks Publication no. 11. Sabah Parks Trustees, Kota Kinabalu. iv + 29 pp.

Tan Fui Lian. 1993. *Checklist of Lizards of Sabah.* Sabah Parks Trustees, Kota Kinabalu. ii + 18 pp.

Tweedie, M.W.F. 1983. *The Snakes of Malaya.* Singapore National Printers (Pte) Ltd., Singapore. (3rd Edition) viii + 167 pp.

Voris, H.K. 1964. *Notes on the Sea Snakes of Sabah.* Sabah Society Journal 2(3): 140–141

Wong, Anna. 1994. *Population Ecology of Amphibians in Different Altitudes of Kinabalu Park.* Sabah Museum Journal 1(2): 29–38

Yates, S. 1992. *The Nature of Borneo.* Facts On File, New York. xvi + 208 pp.

ACKNOWLEDGEMENTS

Most of our work in the field, on which this book is largely based, was carried out in several of Sabah's parks. We are, therefore, especially grateful to the Director of Sabah Parks, Datuk Lamri Ali, for permission to do our research in Kinabalu Park and in Tawau Hills Park. We also wish to express our thanks to the authorities of Sabah Forest Industries and Yayasan Sabah for allowing us to work in areas under their supervision. Field research can be profitable from two points of view— the amount and quality of information gathered, and the pleasure derived from the work itself. Ours has been successful in both ways. For that success, we are indebted to several colleagues and friends who worked with us at various times and provided us with the best of companionship: Alim Biun, Danson Kandaung, Sharon Emerson, Freddy Paulus, Patrick Francis, Paul Yambun, Robert Stuebing, and Harold Voris. Wong Ting Sung and Postar Miun allowed their living turtle specimens to be photographed.

We are also grateful to the following for permission to use their photographs: C.L. Chan, Charles Clarke, P. Hans Hazebroek, Gary Heit, W. Hosmer, Wembley Mogindol, Stephen Von Peltz, W.M. Poon, R.B. Stuebing, Tham Nyip Shen and H.K. Voris.

INDEX

93

Manouria emys 62
masked frog 29
masked tree frog 39, 40
Maticora bivirgata 52
Meristogenys 11, 58, 59, 72, 73,
    76, 88, 58, 59, 72, 73, 88
   kinabaluensis 76
   orphnocnemis 11, 58
Metaphrynella sundana 45
Microhyla borneensis 8
mock viper 47
monitor lizard 12, 79
mossy tree frog 68, 69
mottled cat snake 17
mountain bush frog 66, 67
mountain dwarf litter frog 76
mountain litter frog 74, 75
mountain reed snake 69, 76
mountain torrent frog 76

N

Notochelys platynota 60
Nyctixalus pictus 60, 61

O

Occidozyga laevis 29, 39, 46
olive Ridley sea turtle 24
olive sea snake 22
Ophiophagus hannah 19
Oreocalamus hanitshi 69, 76

P

painted terrapin 25, 26
Pareas laevis 41, 56
Pelochelys bibroni 25
Philautus aurantium 66, 67

   bunitus 66, 67
   ingeri 67
Phoxophrys 72
   nigrilabris 44, 45, 50
pit-viper 16, 19, 20
   keeled Malaysian 17
   leaf-nosed 52, 53
   Sumatran 76
Platyurus platyurus 81
Polypedates colletti 29
   leucomystax 79, 83
   macrotis 39, 40
   otilophus 39, 40
Psammodynastes pulverulentus
   47
Pseudorabdion 31
   collaris 38
Ptychozoon kuhli 44, 45
python 53, 54, 56, 79
   blood 54, 56
   reticulated 53, 56
Python curtus 54, 56
   reticulatus 53, 56

R

rainbow tree snake 53
Rana baramica 29
   blythi 48, 49, 56
   cancrivora 26
   chalconota 48, 49, 56
   erythraea 84
   glandulosa 2, 28, 29
   hosii 8
   ibanorum 8
   ingeri 46, 82
   kuhli 56, 57, 75, 76
   limnocharis 8, 83
   malesiana 34

village brown skink   79, 80

W

Wallace's flying frog   39
white-fronted water snake   30
white-lipped frog   48, 49, 56

X

Xenochrophis trianguligera   31,
     41

Y

yellow-bellied mud frog   29, 39,
     46
yellow-lipped sea krait   21

Z

Zaocys fuscus   53

The authors

Robert F. Inger has been interested in amphibians and reptiles since he was about 10 years old. Inger has worked on amphibians and reptiles in Borneo for many years, doing research on ecological distribution, reproductive behaviour and movements of frogs, temperature relations of lizards, and classification of snakes. Inger is the author of a book on the amphibians of Borneo, co-author of a book on frogs of Sabah, and co-author of a book on the freshwater fishes of Sabah. He was Curator of Amphibians and Reptiles at the Field Museum of Natural History in Chicago, USA; he is now Emeritus Curator.

Tan Fui Lian was born in Sabah and lived there most of her life. She was on the staff of Sabah Parks for 12 years (1980–91), based the entire time in Kinabalu Park. As a park naturalist Tan was responsible for presenting Conservation awareness programmes to school children and other visitors to Kinabalu Park and for bringing such programmes to villages. As staff in the Research and Education Section of Kinabalu Park, Tan assisted many local and foreign scientists who conducted research on plants and animals in the park. At the same time, she was also responsible for the care of the collection of natural history specimens of Sabah Parks. In 1985–1986, she conducted a survey of amphibians in the Kinabalu Park which expanded the Parks' collection. Tan now resides with her husband (Inger) in Chicago where she is Associate in the Division of Amphibians and Reptiles (Zoology Department), Field Museum of Natural History, Chicago.

Inger and Tan began their collaboration in the field in 1987 and those joint efforts have included a survey of the amphibians and reptiles of the Crocker Range National Park (1987–1990) and a project monitoring the populations of frogs in Kinabalu and Tawau Hills Parks, Sabah. They have published several papers resulting from this collaboration as well as this book.